MATCHSTICK IS BACK, JACK!

BY GUS D'ANGELO

*This book is dedicated
to all Boston University students past, present, and future,
to my parents,
and to the memory of John McGuire.*

Published by Boston University

THANKS

My sincere thanks to the following people for making this book possible:

The students, faculty, and administration of Boston University

All editors and staff of *The Daily Free Press*, Fall 1982-Spring 1985

Don Van Natta, Jr. and Ann Loeding for their never-ending support, time, and technical assistance

Laura Freid, editor of *Bostonia* magazine, for her tolerance

The Graphic Art Center of Brookline

Mike "Garbonzo" Cardona, the roommate, rugger, chef and fellow droog who has edited every cartoon for the past three years

All my other friends (you two know who you are)

My most hostile critics, Jim, Pete, and Paul— alias the Brothers D

My parents, Mom and Pop, for the car on weekends and everything else

INTRODUCTION

Dr. John R. Silber
President, Boston University

When Gus D'Angelo asked me to write a preface to this collection of Matchstick cartoons, I knew how Saint Sebastian of Milan felt when the arrow manufacturer asked him for a testimonial.

We can guess that Saint Sebastian, while loving his enemies, might not have gone that far. Now in my case, turning the other cheek is part of my job description. Moreover, it is hard to turn down a request from as engaging and talented a person as Gus. And it occurred to me that Gus didn't say I had to write a respectful preface. He left me entirely free to be as irreverently critical of my youngers and betters as he is of his elders and peers.

Although I toyed with the idea of supplying a devastating— and illustrated— preface that would do unto Matchstick what Matchstick does to the rest of us, I decided upon reflection that I would not. One brilliant satirist is enough within the covers of any one book, and I believe in artistic restraint. Besides, the Lord claims exclusive rights to vengeance.

Additionally, I do not want to be basely ungrateful. In the space of a single year, Gus has promoted me from Grinch to Santa Claus. I don't know whether this means that I am getting nicer or Gus is mellowing with age, (or that he knows something about Santa Claus that the rest of us don't) but in any event, I want to encourage him in this upgrading. Next year, if I play my cards right, I may reappear as George Burns.

But I must point out that Matchstick is a world of fantasy. It is not just a world in which Boston University undergraduates are pigs. It is a place in which the hard-working members of the central administration have time to pass their evenings in the Dugout. I take it as understood that Dean Carter and I have never actually been seen together in the Dugout. Several years ago, two of my assistants— one of whom had infested the Dugout before any of today's undergraduates were born— went there for a quick one after a "Halt the Tuition Hike" rally, an entirely understandable reaction under the circumstances. And the next day there was a letter in the *Free Press* complaining that they were engaged in espionage. If any of the Dugout scenes recorded in Matchstick had actually happened, there would have been either mass demonstrations protesting an administration takeover of a venerable student institution or, less probably, a student boycott.

I am delighted that Matchstick appears here in a format more spacious than the minuscule one which the *Free*

Press, in company with other dailies, now allots to comic strips. Some of the competition, to be sure, print Doonesbury in a size suitable for reading with the naked eye, but the *Free Press*, true to the principle of illegibility, for a time, gave up Doonesbury rather than compromise. I could take that— after all, I could read Doonesbury daily in the less authoritative organ that appears on my doorstep every morning— but I found myself wishing that Matchstick appeared in a size too large for use on postage stamps. In the second term of 1984-85, the *Free Press* began publishing Doonesbury again, and in a show of youthful independence, gave it even more space than its creator demanded. Even the local strips were imperceptibly magnified. Fortunately, one of Gus's more notable talents is to engrave, as it were, comic strips on the heads of pins, and Matchstick is remarkably effective even without a microscope. When, in the early days of this century, comic strips first appeared on Sunday, each was given a full page to itself. That is about the scale Matchstick deserves, and this edition is a step in the right direction.

Looking over the cartoons that follow, it will be readily apparent that Gus D'Angelo has the capacity to outrage all segments of the Boston University community. He also has the power to delight them. The two abilities together prove him a genuine satirist. If the newspaper syndicates of America have any sense, we shall not have heard the last of him.

□

PREFACE

Don Van Natta, Jr.
Editor, *The Daily Free Press*, 1984-1985

On the ever-changing landscape of student-drawn comic strips, few Boston University cartoonists ever aimed their ink pens at the temples of administrator, faculty member and student alike.

But the student creators of such strips as Beetlejuice, Click, Rude Boy, Desmond and Savage Jack all managed to shoot themselves in the foot and out of existence.

It is perhaps an irony that the one cartoonist who dared to irritate the administrative big shot, infuriate the student organization and deflate the ego is still standing tall behind his drawing board.

Matchstick creator/cartoonist/self-proclaimed "Joe Average Student" Gus D'Angelo, a College of Communication senior, portrays what Assistant Dean Joseph Miglio calls "the Boston University conscience."

This is the reason D'Angelo has conquered the challenge of drawing a popular student strip, a feat the Rude Boys and Savage Jacks of the world have only flirted with.

Matchstick *is* back, Jack, for its final hurrah of an illustrious three-year career, simply because D'Angelo uses his pen and wit to take the reader on a *tour de la* vicissitudes of Boston University.

This pen-in-cheek talent has stood the test of time in a topsy-turvy, here-today-gone-tomorrow field. In the process, D'Angelo's strip took third place in a prestigious United- King- Features- Syndicate- judged national collegiate strip contest, making official the irresistibility of the strip 18,500 BU students have turned to for a daily comic respite these three years.

While others were "drawing" Big Wheel-eating characters and pot smoking drug addicts, D'Angelo was depicting BU President John R. Silber and Board of Trustees Chairman Arthur G.B. Metcalf drinking in the Dugout while plotting University real estate acquisitions— in Oklahoma.

Or Dean of Students Ronald L. Carter at home finding a package from the Student Union— a ticking time bomb after he cut $74,000 from its budget.

Or Apathybuster Chris Dolan zapping free-floating apathy vapors for a stipend of $750.

Or...

"I try to draw administrators how they look in the students' eyes," says D'Angelo. "I also ask myself 'How is the BU student mistreated?' Students see themselves hit in the strip the same way they are hit by BU in real life."

This timeliness requires staying in tune with

University news. D'Angelo finds his inspiration by reading "every word" of *The Daily Free Press*, numerous University-published pamphlets and student guides. "I'm probably the only guy on campus who reads *Boston University Today*."

The cartoonist admits he would love to graduate from Boston University and lead the life of Berke Breathed, the Bloom County creator.

"He makes $500,000 a year from his strips, t-shirts and books... He can live wherever he wants in the world, like Bermuda, and it only takes him 10 days to draw a month's worth of strips," D'Angelo says. "That's the life."

That's the life he will shoot for upon graduation in May, 1985. D'Angelo plans to send a portfolio of his work to the major syndicates, though he admits his dream is, well, a dream.

"It's like athletes. I'll try to break into the big time, but I have my degree from BU to fall back upon," says D'Angelo, an Advertising major. "Regardless of what happens, I'll always be drawing."

D'Angelo also predicts he would have no trouble "making the transition" from drawing a strip about BU news to real world news.

"I'd substitute Reagan for Silber, Bush for McCracken..."

The title's origin is as modest as D'Angelo himself.

A "humungous" Memphis State football player in a Memphis bar, "Prince Mongo's," once mistook D'Angelo for making a move on his girlfriend.

He screamed, "Hey, Matchstick, stop talking with my girlfriend" at the red-haired D'Angelo.

"It took two or three days to click that a matchstick is a stick with a red top, which is me," says D'Angelo. "I decided if I'm going to make fun of everyone every day, then I'll poke a little fun at myself in the title.

"It's not really justice, but..."
□

OL' MOM AND POP WEREN'T TOO THRILLED WITH MY FIRST SEMESTER G.P.A....

BUT, I TOLD THEM, "MOM! POP! IT HAPPENS TO ALL FRESHMAN."

SLOWLY, THEY CALMED DOWN.

THANK GOD THEY FORGOT I'M A JUNIOR!

HEY YOU! YES, YOU! SIGN UP NOW FOR MOONIE MARTIAL ARTS!

NO THANKS...

AWWW, C'MON! SIGN UP! BE ONE OF US! STRENGTHEN YOURSELF!

NO! NO! GET LOST!

nudge! nudge!

PLEEEEASE! MOONIE MARTIAL ARTS! JOIN NOW! PROTECT YOURSELF!

OK! OK! WHERE DO I SIGN?

SIR, A SMART MOVE. WHAT CHANGED YOUR MIND?

SO THE NEXT TIME A JERK LIKE YOU APPROACHES ME, I'LL BE ABLE TO PUNCH HIS HEAD IN!

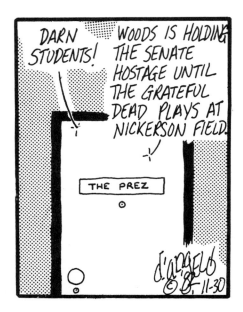

YES KIDDIES! IT'S THAT TIME OF YEAR!

HOW SILBER STOLE CHRISTMAS!

EVERY WHO DOWN IN B.U.-VILLE LIKED CHRISTMAS A LOT...

12-3

BUT THE SILBER WHO LIVED SOUTH OF B.U.-VILLE DID NOT!

bah humbug!

132 CARLTON

SILBER HATED CHRISTMAS AND WITH HIS POSITION, HE WOULD DESTROY THE WHOS' CHRISTMAS AND COLLECT MORE TUITION!

CACKLE! CACKLE!

THE PLOT THICKENS...

HOW SILBER STOLE CHRISTMAS

I KNOW JUST WHAT TO DO SILBER LAUGHED IN HIS THROAT, AND HE MADE A QUICK SANTY CLAUS HAT AND A COAT...

'Tis the season to be greedy!

12-6

THEN SILBER WENT TO B.U.-VILLE WITH SOME OLD EMPTY BAGS, AND HE SLITHERED DOWN WHOS' CHIMNEYS WITHOUT GETTING SNAGGED!

HE TOOK ALL THEIR SCHOLARSHIPS, THEIR LOANS AND THEIR GRANTS, BUT AS HE SENT THE SACKS UP THE CHIMNEY HE FELT A TUG AT HIS PANTS!

THE FEDS?

IT WAS TINY CINDY-B.U. WHO WHO HAD CAUGHT FAKE ST. NICK, SHE HAD LEFT BED FOR ALKA SELZER—ARA. HAD MADE HER QUITE SICK!

sandy claus?

ulp!

HOW SILBER STOLE CHRISTMAS

ACT 3

CINDY-B.U. WHO STARED AT SILBER AND SAID, "SANDY CLAUS, WHY? WHY ARE YOU TAKING OUR MONEY? WHY?"

BUT YOU KNOW OLD SILBER WAS SO SLICK AND SO SWIFT, HE LIED, SAYING, "WHY FOR YOU, MY SWEET! B.U. NEEDS THE LIFT!"

y'know, expenses...

HIS FIB FOOLED THE CHILD AND HE PATTED HER HEAD. HE GAVE HER A CUP OF A.R.A. SWILL AND SENT HER TO BED.

bye sandy claus!

12-7

THEN SILBER WENT UP THE CHIMNEY, HIMSELF, THE OLD CROOK, AND THE ONE SPECK OF CASH THAT HE LEFT IN A NOOK WAS SO USELESS AND SMALL, THAT IT LEFT A WORK STUDY STUDENT WITH VIRTUALLY NOTHING AT ALL!

1¢

THE FAIRY TALE CONTINUES...

HOW SILBER STOLE CHRISTMAS

LAST ACT

SILBER TOOK ALL THE WHOS' MONEY AND MADE A DEPOSIT DOWNTOWN. THEN HE WENT TO B.U.-VILLE TO SMILE AT THE WHOS ALL A-FROWN.

©12-10

BUT, THE WHOS WERE NOT FROWNING, BUT SMILING INSTEAD, AND THEIR SONG OF FRUSTRATION CHANGED SILBER'S HEAD..

*MONEY, IT'S A GAS! GRAB THAT CASH WITH BOTH HANDS AND MAKE A STASH!

*FROM PINK FLOYD

"MAYBE EDUCATION," HE THOUGHT, "ISN'T A BUSINESS. MAYBE EDUCATION... PERHAPS ...SHOUD COST A LOT LESS!" WELL... SILBER BROUGHT BACK THE WHOS' MONEY AND A.R.A. BEAST FOR THE FEAST... AND HE...

...HE HIMSELF...! SILBER CUT THE TUITION!

wait 'till next year!

'00

BOSTON UNIVERSITY TUITION

An ARA poem...
"WAITER! THERE'S A GRASSHOPPER IN MY PORK!"
or
"BE QUIET! EVERYBODY WILL WANT ONE!"
—ACT I—

HI!

ANN ABIGAIL, A RED-HEADED SOPH IN CLA, WENT FOR LUNCH IN SLEEPER HALL AND GRABBED A PLASTIC TRAY...

d'angelo '83 © 2/15

SHE SCANNED THE SELECTION AND THE PORK SANDWICH LOOKED NEAT, SO ANN BROUGHT THE APPETIZING MORSEL TO HER SEAT...

BUT, AS SHE STARTED TO BITE, A MEEK LITTLE VOICE CRIED IN SHEER FRIGHT: "ANN ABIGAIL! DON'T CHEW TOO DEEP! IT'S ME, GARY GRASSHOPPER TRAPPED IN YOUR MEAT!"

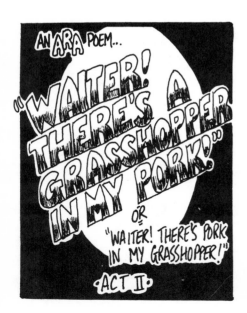

An ARA poem...
"WAITER! THERE'S A GRASSHOPPER IN MY PORK!"
or
"WAITER! THERE'S PORK IN MY GRASSHOPPER!"
—ACT II—

ANN ABIGAIL STARED AT THE BUG IN HER MEAL, AND POKED IT AROUND TO MAKE SURE IT WAS REAL...

vermin!

STAB! STAB! STAB!

THE GRASSHOPPER BEGGED, "PLEASE, ANN, PLEASE WAIT..." THEN STRETCHED OUT HIS LEGS AND STOOD ON HER PLATE. HE SAID:

d'angelo '83 2/16

"MY STORY IS GROSS SO HOLD ONTO YOUR SEAT—IT'S TRUE, ALL A.R.A. FOOD IS GRASSHOPPER MEAT!"

GUEST STAR
ARTHUR G.B. METCALF
CHAIRMAN-BOARD OF TRUSTEES!

d'angelo '83 3/16

CHAIRMAN METCALF, I MUST COMPLIMENT YOU ON YOUR FOLKSY LETTER ANNOUNCING B.U.'s TUITION HIKE. WELL DONE.

THANKS, SILBER. SO WHAT SHALL WE DO WITH OUR NEW-FOUND WEALTH?

AS USUAL, ART, I'VE BEEN EYEING SOME PROPERTY.

KENMORE SQUARE?

NO, OKLAHOMA.

CHIRP! CHIRP! CHIRP!
TWEET! TWEET!
BZZZZZZ!

d'angelo '83

AHHH... BOSTON SPRINGTIME!

WHOMP!

GROAN... BOSTON WEATHER...

IT HAD BEEN A HOT, LONELY SUMMER ON THE B.U. BEACH...

EXCEPT FOR THE RARE INTERNATIONAL STUDENT AND REMEDIAL CBSer, NOT A SOUL HAD SUNNED SINCE SPRING...

NOW, HOWEVER, WE KNOW THE ACADEMIC SEASON HAS RETURNED. HOW?

D'ANGELO '83© 9-19

MATCHSTICK IS BACK, JACK!

WOW! THIS NEW B.U. BOOKSTORE IS AWESOME, AIN'T IT WOODS?

UH... SURE, ZIP.

ALL THE SHOPS! CLOTHES! POSTERS! GOLLY JEEPERS!

9-20 D'ANGELO '83©

THAT'LL BE $257.00.

FOR THREE BOOKS?!

THIS PLACE IS JUST FANTASTIC! WOW!...

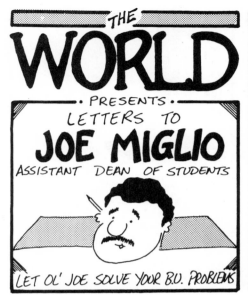

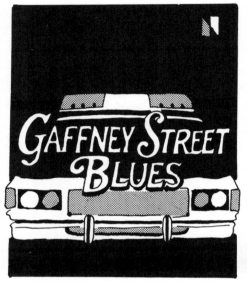

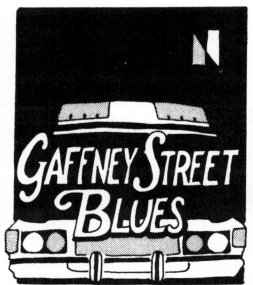

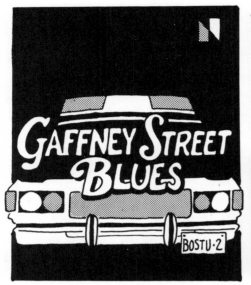

MEANWHILE, AT H.Q.:

I'M SORRY, MA'AM, BUT CONTRARY TO WHAT YOU'VE HEARD, B.U. COPS ONLY RUN ERRANDS FOR B.U. TRUSTEES, NOT FOR LITTLE OLD BROOKLINE LADIES WHO NEED GROCERIES FROM STOP N' SHOP...

UH... YES, MR. SILBER, WE WILL SEND OVER AN OFFICER TO FETCH YOUR PIPE, SLIPPERS, AND NEWSPAPER... YES... IMMEDIATELY...

11/9

LISTEN! I UNDERSTAND THAT YOU'VE BEEN ROBBED, STABBED, AND SHOT. BUT, WE HAVE PRIORITIES, KID. WHEN DETECTIVE GOLDBLOOM FINISHES WALKING THE TRUSTEE'S DOG, WE'LL RUSH OVER...

D'ANGELO '85 ©

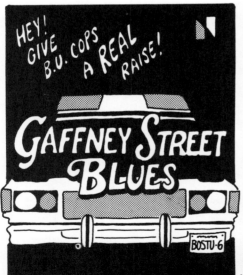

HEY! GIVE B.U. COPS A REAL RAISE!

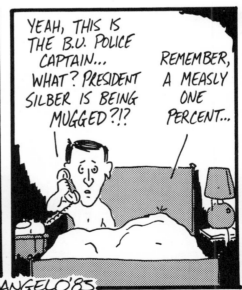

DAMN BOSTON U! JOYCE, AFTER CREATING AN OASIS OF SAFETY IN BOSTON'S CRIME DESERT, US B.U. COPS GET A MEASLY 1% RAISE!

RING!

QUIT BROODING, FRANK, AND ANSWER THE PHONE...

11/10

YEAH, THIS IS THE B.U. POLICE CAPTAIN... WHAT? PRESIDENT SILBER IS BEING MUGGED?!?

REMEMBER, A MEASLY ONE PERCENT...

© D'ANGELO '85

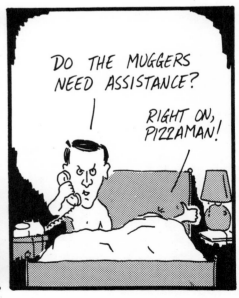

DO THE MUGGERS NEED ASSISTANCE?

RIGHT ON, PIZZAMAN!

THIS IS HO-WARD CO-SELL LIVE AT THE ORANGE BOWL....

"TODAY, #1 RATED NEBRASKA MEETS DIVISION 1-AA POWERHOUSE BOSTON UNIVERSITY..."

"THE TERRIERS ARE DEFINITE UNDERDOGS. B.U.'s OBSTACLES INCLUDE THEIR USUAL FAN SUPPORT, ... "

B.U.

BOSTON U

11/30

DANGELO 83 ©

"...THE FORMIDABLE TASK OF STOPPING NEBRASKA'S "TEAM OF THE CENTURY,"...

CORNHUSKERS
73

"...AND A SLIGHT SIZE DISCREPANCY..."

Uh...nice doggie...

BOSTON

N
O

IT HAS BEEN AN UPSET, LA-DIES AND GENTLEMEN. YES, BOSTON U. HAS PUMMELED #1 NEBRASKA!

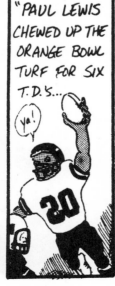

"PAUL LEWIS CHEWED UP THE ORANGE BOWL TURF FOR SIX T.D.'S...

ya!

20

"AIR ENGLISH WITH HARTFORD AND BROOKS ADDED FOUR MORE THROUGH THE AIR...

"AND 'EGAN'S WRECKING CREW' HIT NEBRASKA'S STARS TURNER GILL AND MIKE ROZIER...THEIR JERSIES HAD AN IDENTITY CRISIS...

0   0

"BOSTON UNIVERSITY HAS PULLED THE VICTORY OF THE CENTURY! B.U. STUDENTS WATCHING BACK HOME MUST BE ECSTATIC!"

TERRIERS   CORNHUSKERS

"THREE'S COMPANY WILL RETURN AFTER THESE MESSAGES..."

12/1

© DANGELO 83

1984
·OR·

BIG SILBER
IS WATCHING YOU.

PART I

BOSTON UNIVERSITY, 1984. WINSTON SMITH, A SENIOR, HAS SEEN MANY CHANGES SINCE HIS FRESHMANHOOD...

THE ADMINISTRATION'S ATTEMPT TO LIMIT THE STUDENTS' FREEDOMS HAS LED TO CAMERAS IN THE DORMS...

©D'ANGELO'81

THEN, THE IMPLEMENTATION OF "B.U. SPEAK," A LANGUAGE BASED UPON THE THREE FANATICAL SLOGANS OF BIG SILBER:

TUITION IS JOB
B.U. IS EDUCATION
YOU ARE IMPORTANT.

1984

BIG SILBER
IS WATCHING YOU.

PART II

WITH "B.U. SPEAK," BIG SILBER AND THE INNER PARTY SLOWLY ELIMINATED THE FREEDOMS AND HAPPINESS OF THE STUDENTS...

WHERE ARE THE CONCERTS AND DANCES AND BLOCK PARTIES?

THE STUDENT GOVERNMENT WAS LEFT POWERLESS AND ITS MONIES USURPED...

WHERE IS THE "STUDENT ACTIVITIES FEE?" HUH?

©D'ANGELO'81   11/25

BIG SILBER EVEN RESTRICTED FRIENDSHIP, MAKING IT IMPOSSIBLE TO VISIT A FRIEND IN ANOTHER DORM WITHOUT A HASSLE:

SORRY, BABE, YOU'VE ALREADY SIGNED-IN THREE PEOPLE. NO MORE.

1984

BIG SILBER IS WATCHING YOU.

Although Winston has signed in three friends, he sneaks in a fourth, Julia, and therefore violates Big Silber's limit on dorm friendships. In Winston's room, he and Julia curse the oppressive Big Silber:

DOWN WITH BIG SILBER!

Julia, however, has been seen by the dorm cameras. The thought police legally search Winston's room...

A-HA! I FOUND HER!

Winston is dragged to Room 101, the place where enemies of Big Silber are punished...

ROOM 101
OFFICE OF THE DEAN OF STUDENTS
MINISTRY OF LOVE.

1984

Winston Smith was sent to Room 101 to be punished for violating the laws of Big Silber. In Room 101, Winston faces Comrade O'Carter who dishes out the verdict...

Guilty! Oh-sooo guilty! Winston, you will receive maximum torture!! You will be force-fed A.R.A. leftovers!

...oh god no...

So, Winston suffered, suffered until he obediently believed in the slogans of Big Silber—tuition is job B.U. is education you are important.

Maybe you have not yet been brainwashed, but watch out!

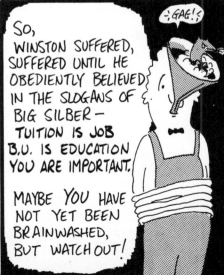

GAG!

Remember...

BIG SILBER IS WATCHING YOU.

MATCHSTICK presents...

B.U.oodles!

Guess what the following Drawings represent! ➔

#1.

#2.

twiddle! twiddle!

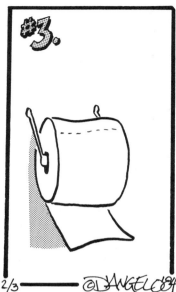

#3.

ANSWERS:

#1- THE COMM. AVE. TROLLEY IN ACTION.

#2- OUR STUDENT UNION IN SESSION.

#3- A CONSTRUCTIVE USE OF THE B.U. <u>WORLD</u>.

2/3 ———— ©D'ANGELO '84

DUGOUT

OLÁ, ZIP! OOO-BOY, ROUGH NIGHT, EH? YOU'VE POLISHED OFF PLENTY MILK.

I'M DROWNING MY SORROWS, JORDINO.

AH! ZIP, I THINK I KNOW WHY YOU ARE SO DEPRESSED.

YEAH?

SÍ. YOU GOTTA NO GIRL. WHEN WAS THE LAST TIME YOU WENT ON A DATE?

1973.

2/7 ©D'ANGELO '84

YOUR PROBLEM, ZIP, IS THAT YOU HAVE NO LATINO BLOOD, THEREFORE, NO ROMANCE.

SO HOW DO I LEARN TO SPEAK ROMANTICALLY?

EASY. I TEACH. REPEAT: "ERES MÁS FÉA QUE UNA PATADA EN LAS PELOTAS."

WHICH MEANS?

WHO CARES? AMERICAN GIRLS WON'T UNDERSTAND. IT SOUNDS ROMANTIC.

AHHH!

JORDINO! THE SPANISH PICK-UP LINES AREN'T WORKING. CAN I TRY ENGLISH ON THE NEXT GIRL?

UH, ZIP... BE CAREFUL...

YOO-HOO! I'M ZIP! DO YOU COME HERE OFTEN?

UH (HIC!)...YUP... LOTS...(BURP!) UH... I FEEL... ⇋PUKE⇋

JORDINO? SHOULD I MOVE ON TO A GIRL THAT'S CONSCIOUS?

UHHH... SÍ. BUT, CHANGE YOUR SHIRT FIRST...

ODE TO SPRING.

3/30

SPRINGTIME IN BOSTON,
ISN'T IT NICE?
FOUR INCHES OF SNOW
HIDE A LAYER OF ICE.

THE WIND HOWLS AND BLOWS
WITH THE RAIN, SNOW, AND SLEET,
AND MANGLED UMBRELLAS
LIE DEAD IN THE STREET.

AS FOR BRIGHT AND WARM SUNSHINE,
THERE IS NO SUCH THING.
ONLY TOE-FREEZING SLUSH.
HEY, DON'T YOU LOVE SPRING?

SO, WALTER, IS IT TRUE
THAT B.U. HOCKEY PLAYERS
HAVE BECOME SO POPULAR
THAT THEIR NAMES ARE
NOW B.U. JARGON?

YEP,
WATCH...

HEY, FRANK!
HOW WAS
YOUR DATE?

DON'T ASK.
IT WAS
A "CLEON."

HOW CAN
A DATE
BE A "CLEON,"
WALT?

EASY...

A "CLEON" IS
WHEN YOU JUST
CAN'T SCORE...

ZIP, ONE PROBLEM YOU HAVE WITH PICKING UP GIRLS IS YOUR PHYSIQUE. STAND UP...

O.K., JORDINO...

3/20

LOOK! WHAT GIRL WANTS TO GO OUT WITH THE PILSBURY DOUGH BOY? HUH? MAKE A MUSCLE...

ULP...

PRETTY FLABBY, ZIP, PRETTY FLABBY...

JORDINO WAS RIGHT. IF MY LOVE LIFE IS TO IMPROVE, I MUST GET IN SHAPE. WELP, HERE'S THE B.U. WEIGHT ROOM.

UM... A FRIEND OF MINE TOLD ME TO GET LIFTING ADVICE FROM A MISTER NUMA?

THAT-A-WAY...

HI, I'M NUMA. YOU MUST BE JORDINO'S WIMPY FRIEND, ZIP. DON'T WORRY, I'LL MAKE A CHARLES ATLAS OF YOU YET! LET'S START WITH BENCH PRESS...

SUPER!

3/21

NOW, ZIP! LIFT!

OOOMPH! UG! GASP! NUMA, I CAN'T. WE BETTER TRY A LIGHTER WEIGHT.

...ZIP, TEN POUNDS IS AS LIGHT AS YOU CAN GO...

HEY, YOU
GUYS ARE SUPER.
REALLY.

C'MON, ZIP! JOIN UP WITH ME. WE'LL HAVE A GOOD TIME!

..welp...

... I DUNNO, BARRY, I JUST DON'T KNOW...

WELL, ZIP, IF YOU DON'T JOIN WITH ME, I WON'T BE YOUR FRIEND ANYMORE.

...sigh...

WELL, BOYS, WELCOME TO PHI AMA FOOL, "THE FRAT WHERE IT'S AT!"

FOR RUSH, YOU THREE UNFORTUNATES MUST ACT AS IF YOU ARE ONE PERSON, MEANING, YOU WILL DO EVERYTHING TOGETHER.

EVERYTHING???

...YEP, EVERYTHING...

MEN

MATCHSTICK is once again proud to present...

BUoodles!

Guess what the following drawings represent ⟶

#1.

#2.

#3.

ANSWERS:

#1 - WTBU.

#2 - THE 8.4% TUITION INCREASE.

#3 - SILBER'S CENTRAL AMERICAN SOLUTION.

HOCKEY MINSTRELS:

HEY-HEY T.J., WHAT DO YOU SAY?

WE GONNA GUTTER BOWLING GREEN IN THE N-C-A-A...

"...CLEON'LL GUARD THE NET AN' CULLEN'LL POP EM' IN, THEN WE'LL CRUISE TO THE DUGOUT TO SAVOR OUR WIN!"

DOO - WAAAAAH!

the Private i

"THIS PROMISCUOUS THING HAD GOTTEN BIG ON CAMPUS. REAL BIG. BOSTON U HAD BEEN LABELED THE "MOST PROMISCUOUS" COLLEGE CAMPUS IN LISA BIRNBACH'S COLLEGE BOOK..."

"IT WAS MY JOB, AS B.U.'S PRIVATE INVESTIGATOR, TO FIND THE STUDENTS WHO HAD LED MS. BIRNBACH TO THIS CONCLUSION..."

"ENTER ARTHUR SHLOTZ, SOPHOMORE..."

HEY, I WAS AN INEXPERIENCED FROSH AT THE TIME. DESPERATE, TOO...

SO, I GAVE THIS WOMAN THE EYE, Y'KNOW. LIKE, I DIDN'T KNOW SHE WAS A WRITER...

SHE LOOKED LIKE SOME KIND OF NYMPHO TO ME. REMEMBER, I WAS A DESPERATE FRESHMAN AND, LISA WAS SOOOO EASY...

9/18 ©DANGELO '84

Private i

"LISA 'DO ANYTHING FOR A BUCK' BIRNBACH BASED HER OPINION OF B.U. AS "MOST PROMISCUOUS" UPON ONE NIGHT WITH ARTHUR SHLOTZ, THEN A B.U. FRESHMAN..."

O.K., SHLOTZ, 3 DECEMBER '83...

ulp...

WELL, I PICKED UP LISA AT A FRAT PARTY AND WE WENT BACK TO MY ROOM IN C-TOWER WHERE... WE... WELL...

WOW! OOO! OOO! YEAH!

UM... ARTHUR, DEAR, IT'S MORE FUN IF I JOIN YOU...

...oh...

9/19 ©DANGELO '84

Private i

"THE CASE WAS TAKING SHAPE... DECEMBER 3, 1983. LISA BIRNBACH, AUTHOR OF THE COLLEGE BOOK, SEDUCED INEXPERIENCED AND DESPERATE FROSH ARTHUR SHLOTZ FOR RESEARCH PURPOSES..."

O.K., SHLOTZ, THEN WHAT?

well...erp...

9/20   ©D'ANGELO '84

THAT WAS IT?!?

YEP. GET LOST, KID, I GOT MORE RESEARCH TO CONDUCT.

BUT, LISA, WHAT ABOUT LOVE? FEELING? COMMITMENT?

NEXT! NUMBER 36!

WAIT... DON'T I GET A CIGARETTE OR SOMETHING?

Private i

"EPILOGUE:
   ARTHUR SHLOTZ, SOPHOMORE, HAD THE INTIMATE ENCOUNTER WITH LISA BIRNBACH WHICH LED HER TO LABEL B.U. AS 'MOST PROMISCUOUS'. MY INTERROGATION HAD GOTTEN EMOTIONAL..."

9/21   ©D'ANGELO '84

YOU MEAN TO SAY, SHLOTZ, THAT YOU RISKED THE ACADEMIC CREDIBILITY OF B.U. UPON ONE SLEAZY FLING?

HEY, I DIDN'T KNOW THE NYMPHO WAS A JOURNALIST! I WAS USED!

UM... ART... BETWEEN YOU AND ME, HOW WAS MS. BIRNBACH BETWEEN THE SHEETS? HUH?

A BEACHED WHALE, MR. i, A BEACHED WHALE.

Apathybuster-busters.

10/16

THE APATHYBUSTERS ADVERTISED ON 'TBU AND LOCAL T.V.:

WE'RE READY TO DECEIVE YOU!

X3635

SONY

THEIR FIRST JOB WAS AN APATHY GHOUL LOOSE IN THE G.S.U. BALLROOM...

GOT 'IM!

ZAP

YOW!

EXTERMINATION. THAT'LL BE $750 PER WORKER.

YOU SWINDLER! GIMME BACK THE APATHY!

Apathybuster-busters

AS THEIR FAME GREW, THE APATHYBUSTERS RACED AROUND CAMPUS, BUSTING APATHY...

YAA!

10/17

MEANWHILE, AT A STAFF PARTY THROWN BY DARYL DELUCA OF RESIDENCE LIFE...

Oh, sure, I stomped on students today...

MY HERO!

AN APATHY DEMON HID IN DARYL'S CLOSET...

grrrr!

AND THEN POUNCED UPON DARYL, INFESTING HIM WITH AN INTENSE HATRED OF BANDS, PARTIES, & DANCES:

WHERE IS GOZER?? I AM THE KEYMASTER!!!

OH GOD NO!

Apathybuster busters.

IN SEARCH OF GOZER THE APATHY SPIRIT, DARYL DELUCA CLIMBS TO THE TOP OF THE LAW SCHOOL...!

SUDDENLY, THE APATHYBUSTERS APPEAR BELOW TO DESTROY THE FESTERING APATHY ABOVE!

Sorry, no autographs

UPON REACHING THE ROOF: OH NO! DARYL'S GONE! CHRIS, THAT MEANS THAT GOZER WILL REAPPEAR IN THE FORM OF THE FIRST THING THAT POPS INTO OUR MINDS!

©DANGELO'84 10/17

oh shi...

DEAN CARTER AS THE STAY PUFT MAN!

STAY PUFT

"AAAAAAAAA!!"

WHEN THE APATHY'S RUNNIN' THROUGH YOUR DORM, AND COLLEGE LIFE JUST AIN'T THE NORM, WHO YA' GONNA CALL??

APATHY BUSTERS!

MEAN DEAN RON

WHEN YA' WANNA BURN A BIG TEN THOU, AND YOU JUST AIN'T SURE EXACTLY HOW, WHO YA GONNA CALL??

...apathy busters...

DOCTOR J.R. 10/18

MAKIN' MONEY MAKES US FEEL GOOD!

©DANGELO'84

I CAN'T HEEEAR YOU!

Frivolous Pursuits

THIS IS HOWARD CO-SELL FOR THE 1st ANNUAL B.U. TRIVIAL PURSUIT. THE CONTESTANTS:

"MEAN" DEAN CARTER. KNOWN TO INTIMIDATE HIS OPPONENTS EARLY ON. IDOLIZES CLINT EASTWOOD...

DARYL "THE HIT MAN" DeLUCA. HIS WEAKNESS IS ENTERTAINMENT. HE JUST DOESN'T KNOW WHAT IT IS...

TRUSTEE CHAIRMAN ART "CHECKBOOK" METCALF. PLAYS FOR BIG STAKES...

10/29

JOHN "THE PREZ" SILBER. LOVES GEOGRAPHY TRIVIA AND COLLECTING THE SLICES...

Frivolous Pursuits

LET THE GAMES BEGIN...

"MEAN DEAN RON ROLLS FIRST...

© DANGELO '84   10/30

"HE LANDS UPON ART AND LITERATURE."

"UPON WHAT EVENT DID PABLO PICASSO BASE HIS PAINTING GUERNICA, A PAINTING OF PEOPLE WITH STICKS, DYING HORSES, AND DISMAL DARKNESS?"

THE SPANISH CIVIL WAR!!

"WRONG. RICH HALL ON SATURDAY NIGHT."

DAMN!

JOHN SILBER LANDS ON SPORTS. MEAN DEAN RON ASKS THE QUESTION:

WHAT COLLEGE FOOTBALL TEAM HAS WON 4 OUT OF ITS LAST 5 LEAGUE TITLES?

UM... WELL... GEE... OH YEAH! U.S.C.!!

HA! YOU ARE WRONG! IT'S BOSTON U.!

DAMMIT! NOBODY KNOWS THAT! GIMMIE MY WEDGE!

urp!

11/1 ©D'ANGELO'84

Y'KNOW, TIM, EVERY YEAR I COME BACK TO THE 'OL ALMA MATER...

WELCOME ALUMNI

EACH YEAR THE PLACE IS DIFFERENT. Y'KNOW, THE NAMES, THE FACES, THE FASHIONS. BUT, ONE ASPECT HAS REMAINED THE SAME EVER SINCE I WAS AN SMG FROSH.

©D'ANGELO'84 ALUMNI

AND THAT IS?

WELCOME ALUMNI

B.U. STILL WANTS MY MONEY.

WELCOME ALUMONEY

MATCHSTICK presents...

HOMECOMING

B.U.oodles!

Guess what the following drawings represent →

#1.

#2.

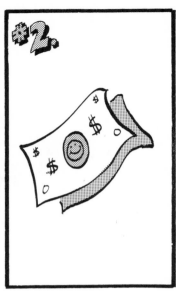

#3.

Ken'l rations

©DANGELO'84 — 11/5

ANSWERS:

#1 – HOW B.U. TREATED HOLY CROSS.

#2 – WHY MOM AND DAD WERE INVITED.

#3 – WHAT WAS SERVED AT THE POST-GAME KENNEL CLUB.

WHAT DO YOU GET WHEN YOU CROSS A UNIQUE, INNOVATIVE, AND ARTISTIC COMIC STRIP...

WITH A YOUNG CARTOONIST, WHO, BY HIS OWN NAIVETÉ, STEPS OVER THE BOUNDS OF GOOD TASTE...

...oops, sorry...

KENT DANISH

AND THEN WITH A FANATIC BAND OF YOUNG REPUBLICAN PUPPETS AND CONFUSED NEWSPAPER EDITORS?

JUSTICE ???

ISH
—o—
1984

11/14   ©D'ANGELO 84

YEAH! TONY! YEAH!

ERIC'S GYM

LIFT IT, NUMA, LIFT IT!

NB

©D'ANGELO 84   10/22

GO, LOIS, GO!

...give it up, pal...

BOSTON UNIVERSITY